Tiger Tales 2
My Progress Journal

My Language Passport	2
How are you, Tiger!	3
1. **A Surprise**	4
2. **A New Pet**	6
3. **Where's my coat?**	8
4. **Break Time**	10
5. **What's the matter?**	12
6. **On Holiday**	14

Carol Read • Mark Ormerod

My Language Passport

Tell me about you!

Stick your photo here.

My name: _____

My age: _____

My school: _____

My class: _____

My teacher's name: _____

Languages I speak: _____

Languages I'm learning: _____

How are you, Tiger?

My learning review

1. ✏️ Circle the animals red, the toys blue and the foods yellow. 💬 Say.

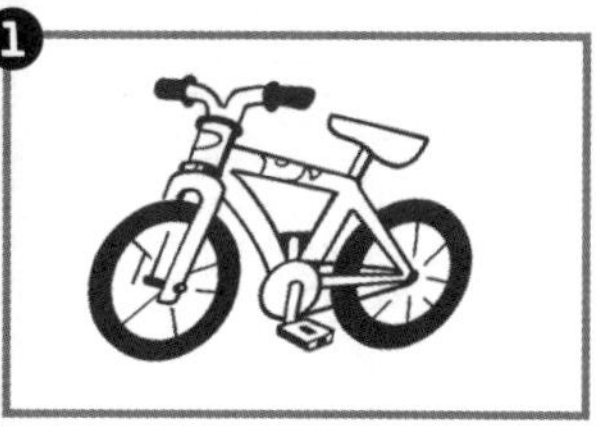

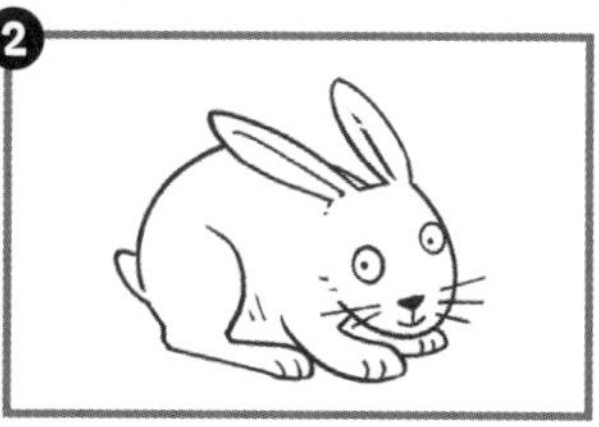

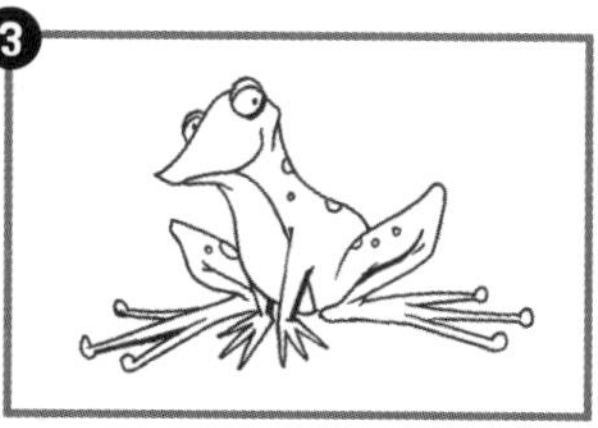

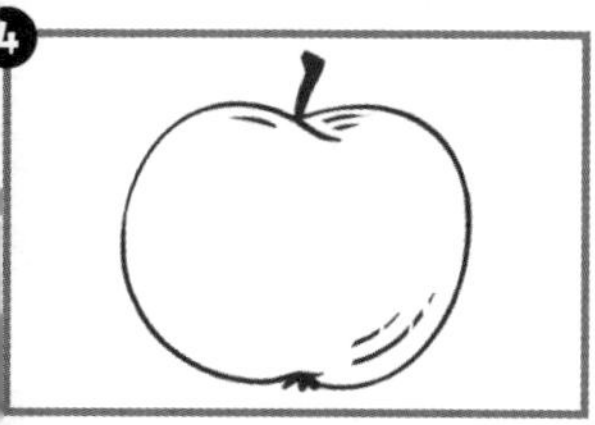

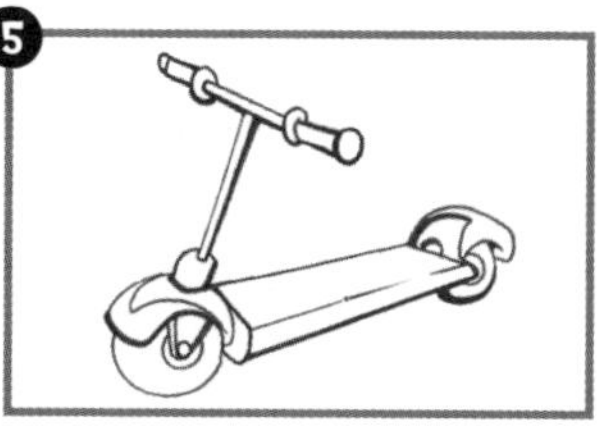

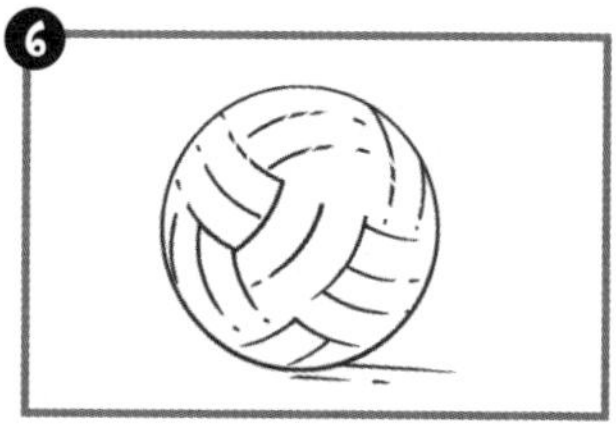

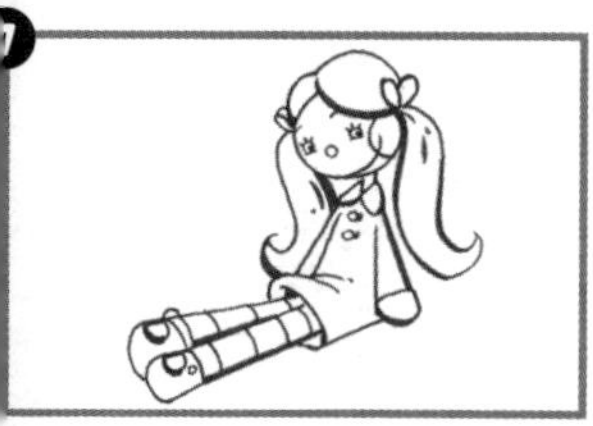

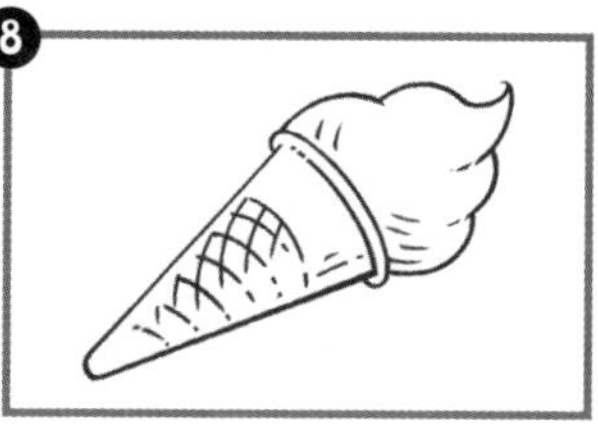

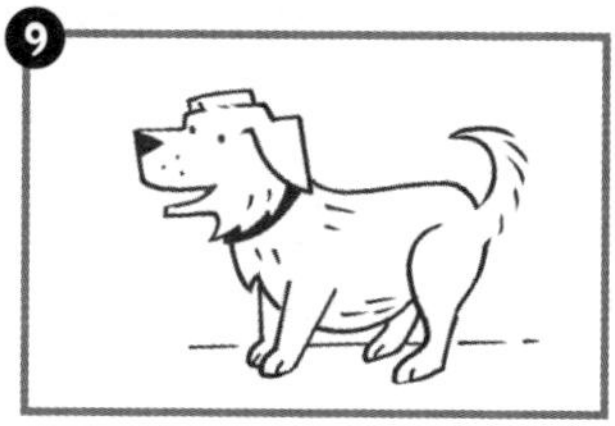

2. 🖍️ Colour the numbers you know. 💬 Tell a friend.

Number 10 is grey.

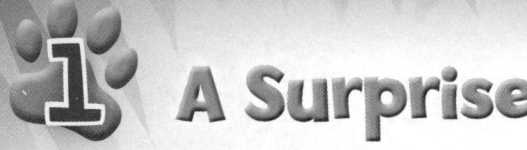

A Surprise

My learning review

1 ✏️ **Colour your favourite part of the unit.** 💬 **Tell a friend**

Story | Songs | Kids' Culture

2 💬 ✏️ **Say, match and write.**

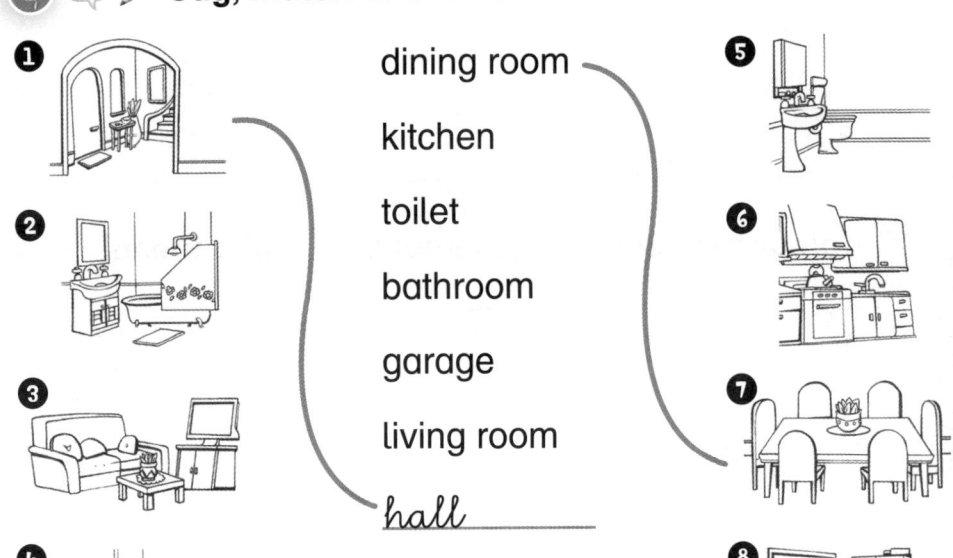

dining room
kitchen
toilet
bathroom
garage
living room
hall

My progress

3 ✏ **Look, think and colour Tiger's paws.**

I can …

❶ ❷

❸ ❹ sofa

❺ In my bedroom… ❻

Learning to LEARN My study ideas

4 ✏ **Look and tick (✔) what you do.**   Where's my pen?

My score for Unit 1: / 10

Key: I can ❶ use the online materials, ❷ understand and act out the story, ❸ sing the songs,
❹ identify vocabulary items by listening, ❺ talk about my bedroom, ❻ compare types of homes in the UK and my country.
My study ideas: Key: ❶ I listen to the songs at home. ❷ I speak English in class.

2 A New Pet

My learning review

online materials

1 Colour your favourite part of the unit. Tell a friend.

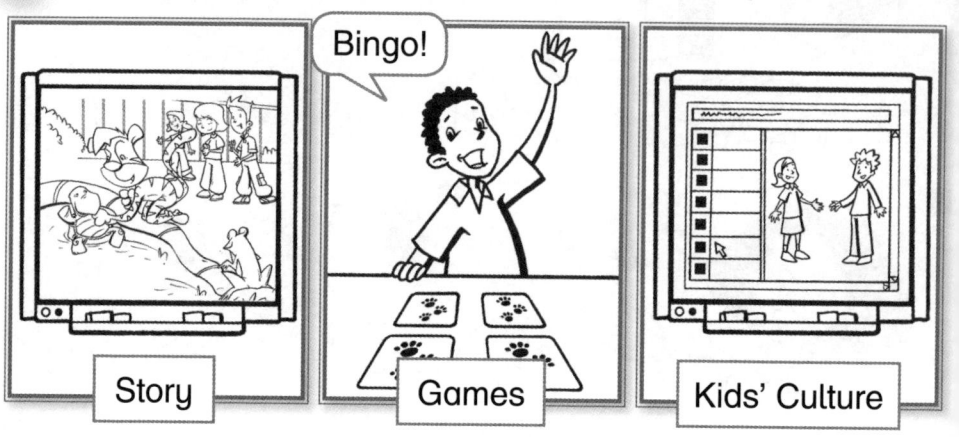

Story

Bingo!
Games

Kids' Culture

2 Say, match and write.

1

2

3

4

lizard

kitten

turtle

hamster

bird

fish

puppy ________

____

5

6

7

8

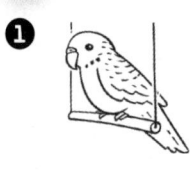

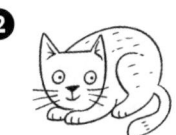

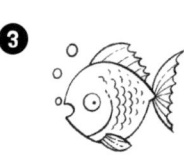

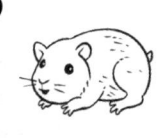

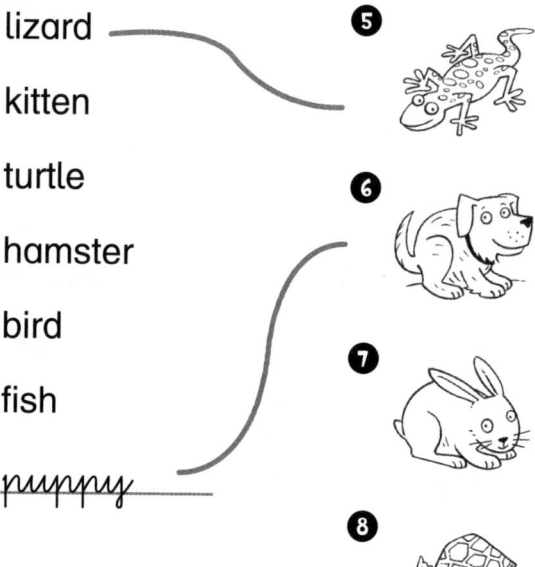

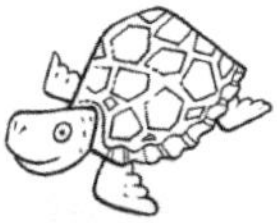

My progress

3 ✏ **Look, think and colour Tiger's paws.**

I can …

❶ ❷

❸ ❹

❺ ❻

My study ideas

4 ✏ **Look and tick (✓) what you do.**

My score for Unit 2: / 10

Key: I can ❶ use the online materials, ❷ understand and act out the story, ❸ sing the songs, ❹ do the role play, ❺ talk about what pets eat, ❻ say and act out a traditional rhyme.
My study ideas: Key: ❶ I listen to the teacher. ❷ I use the online materials at home.

3 Where's my coat?

My learning review

online materials

1 Colour your favourite part of the unit. Tell a friend.

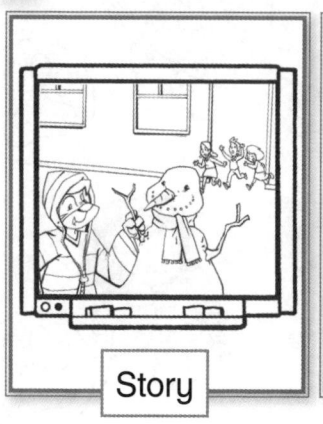

Story

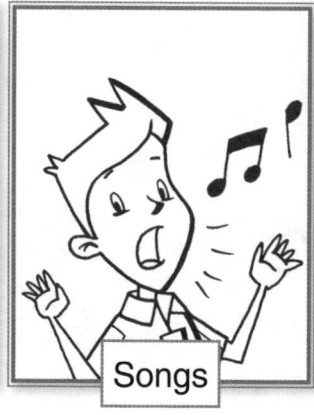

Songs

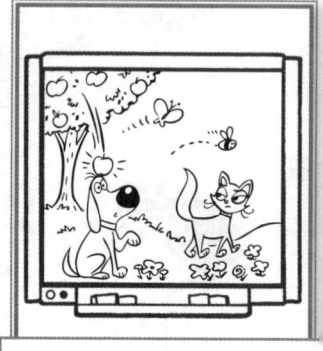

Ping and Pong story

2 Say, match and write.

1

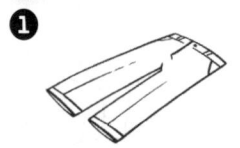

2

3 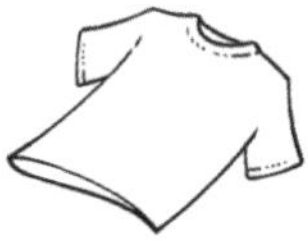

4

trousers

T-shirt

jumper

shoes and socks

shirt

skirt

______

______

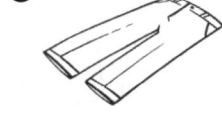

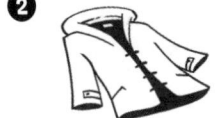

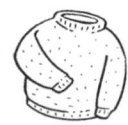

5

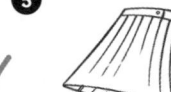

6

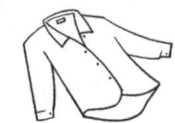

7

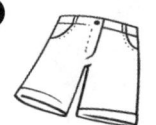

8

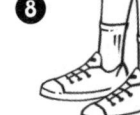

My progress

3 ✏️ **Look, think and colour Tiger's paws.**

I can …

❶ T-shirt ❷

❸ ❹

❺ ❻ My favourite season is…

My study ideas

4 ✏️ **Look and tick (✔) what you do.**

❶ ❷

My score for Unit 3: / 10

Key: I can ❶ associate pictures with meaning, ❷ use the online materials, ❸ understand and act out the story,
❹ sing the songs, ❺ do the role play, ❻ talk about my favourite season.
My study ideas: Key: ❶ I help my classmates. ❷ I show my work to my family.

Break Time

My learning review

1. Colour your favourite part of the unit. Tell a friend.

Story   Songs   Kids' Culture

2. Say, match and write.

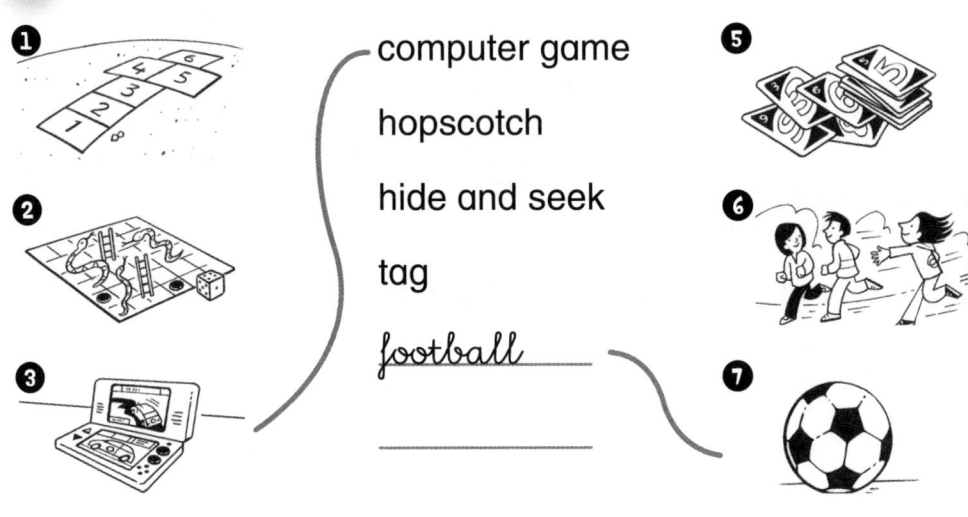

computer game

hopscotch

hide and seek

tag

football

_____

_____

My progress

3 ✏️ **Look, think and colour Tiger's paws.**

I can …

① ②  ③  ④  ⑤  ⑥

My study ideas

4 ✏️ **Look and tick (✔) what you do.**

My score for Unit 4: / 10

Key: I can ① use the online materials, ② understand and act out the story, ③ express an opinion about the story, ④ sing the songs, ⑤ play games with the cut-outs, ⑥ play a traditional game.
My study ideas: Key: ① I complete activities with care. ② I ask if I need help.

5 What's the matter?

My learning review

online materials

1 Colour your favourite part of the unit. Tell a friend.

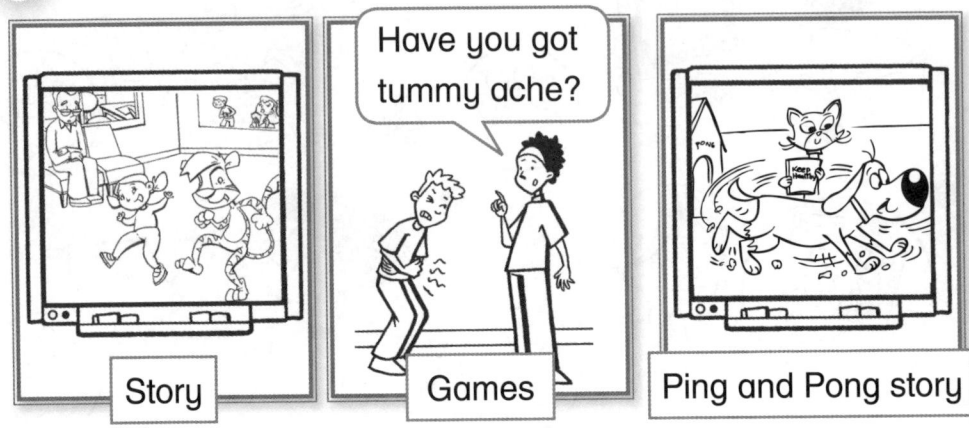

Story

Games

Ping and Pong story

2 Say, match and write.

1

2

3

4

sore throat

tummy ache

cough

____

____

____

____

____

5 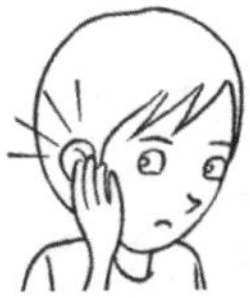

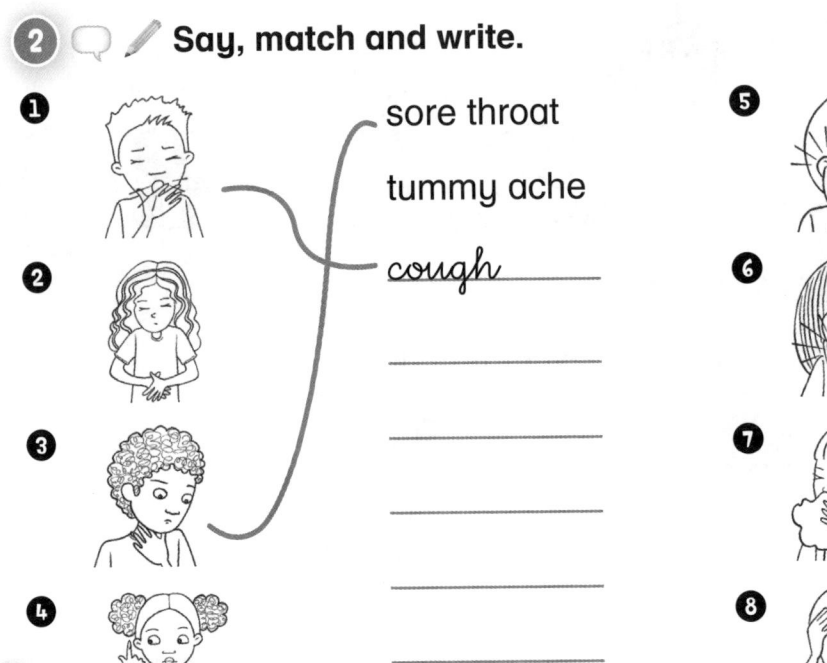

6 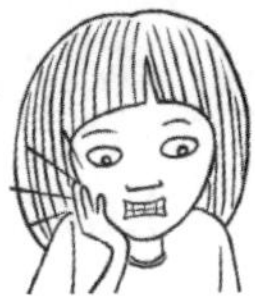

7 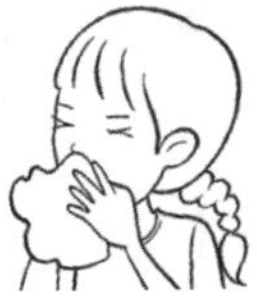

8 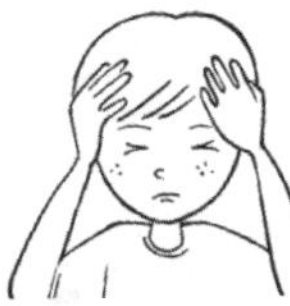

My progress

3 ✏️ **Look, think and colour Tiger's paws.**

I can …

❶ ❷

❸ ❹

❺ ❻ Doctor, doctor …

Learning to LEARN — My study ideas

4 ✏️ **Look and tick (✓) what you do.**

tummy ache, tummy ache

My score for Unit 5:   / 10

Key: I can ❶ use the online materials, ❷ understand and act out the story, ❸ sing the songs, ❹ do a role play, ❺ review and reflect on learning, ❻ act out a traditional joke.
My study ideas: Key: ❶ I look after my book. ❷ I repeat words and phrases.

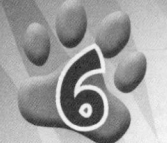

6 On Holiday

My learning review

online materials

1 Colour your favourite part of the unit. Tell a friend.

Story

Songs

Kids' Culture

2 Say, match and write.

1 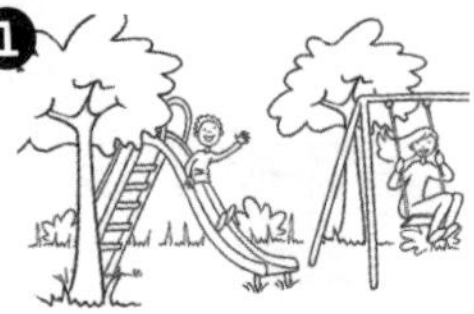

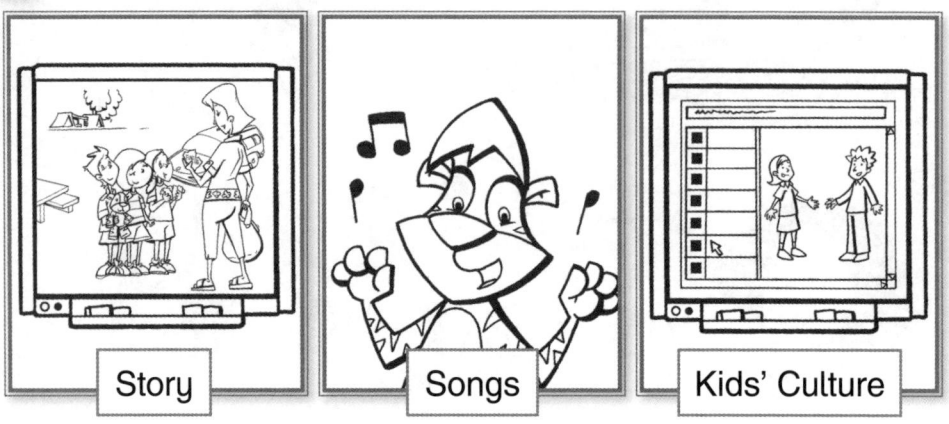

2 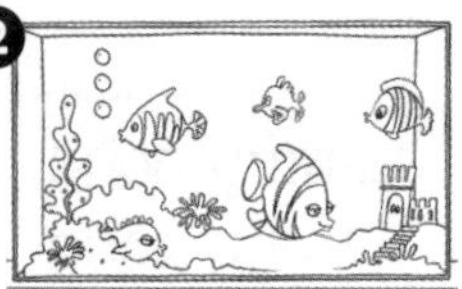

3 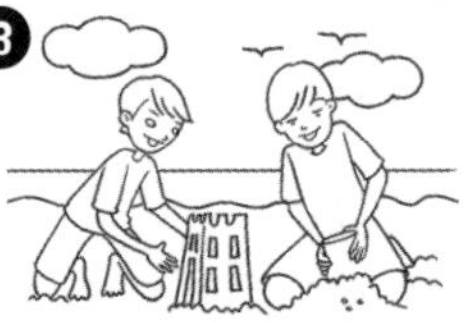

4 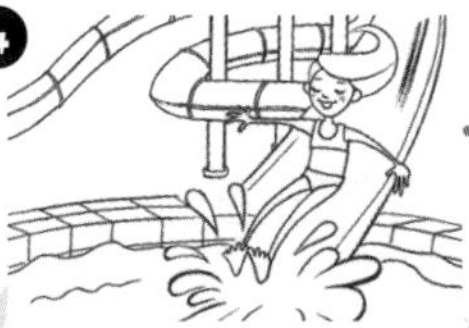

water park

aquarium

zoo

____

____

____

____

____

5 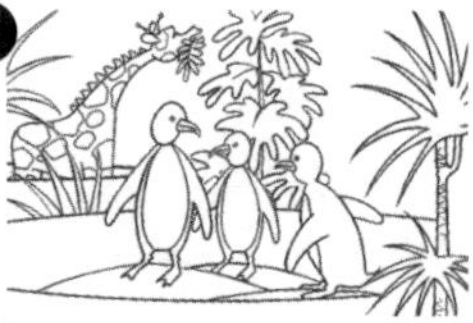

6 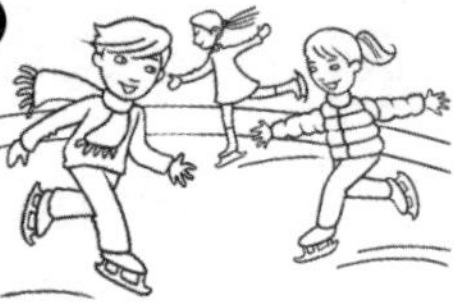

7 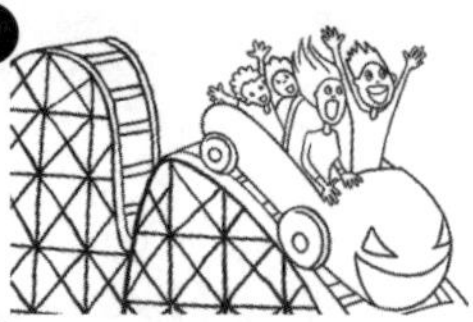

8 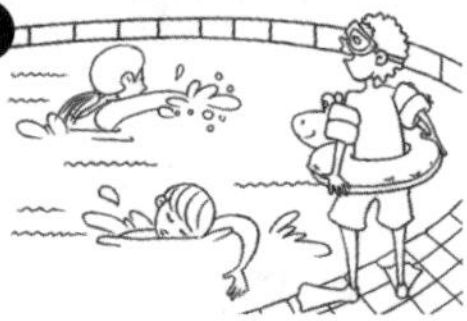

My progress

3 ✏ **Look, think and colour Tiger's paws.**

I can …

My study ideas

4 ✏ **Look and tick (✓) what you do.**

My score for Unit 6: / 10

Key: I can ❶ use the online materials, ❷ understand and act out the story, ❸ sing the songs,
❹ use classroom language, ❺ act out a road safety sequence, ❻ recognise and write key words.
My study ideas: Key: ❶ I review my learning. ❷ I listen to the songs and watch the storyteller at home.

Macmillan Education
4 Crinan Street
London N1 9XW
A division of Springer Nature Limited
Companies and representatives throughout the world

ISBN 978 0 230 43087 7

Text © Carol Read and Mark Ormerod 2013
Design and illustration © Springer Nature Limited 2013

First published 2013

All rights reserved; no part of this publication may be reproduced, stored in a retrieval system, transmitted in any form, or by any means, electronic, mechanical, photocopying, recording, or otherwise, without the prior written permission of the publishers.

These materials may contain links for third party websites. We have no control over, and are not responsible for, the contents of such third party websites. Please use care when accessing them.

Although we have tried to trace and contact copyright holders before publication, in some cases this has not been possible. If contacted we will be pleased to rectify any errors or omissions at the earliest opportunity.

Designed by Blooberry Design Ltd
Illustrated by Adrian Barclay, Rodrigo Folgueira and Simon Walmesley
Cover design by Astwood Design Consultancy
Cover photographs by Macmillan Publishers Ltd / Stuart Cox
Cover illustration by Rodrigo Folgueira

Printed and bound in Uruguay

2019
2 6